Star Bores

by Steve Barlow and Steve Skidmore

Illustrated by Geo Parkin

MELVYN

Age	14.
Likes	Trainspotting and model making.
Dislikes	Sport.
Character	Nerd. Clever, but not as clever as he thinks he is.

FERGUS

Age	14.
Likes	Trivial facts and milk bottle top collecting.
Dislikes	Anything too exciting.
Character	Nerd. Softies don't come any softer.

RODNEY

Age	14.
Likes	Stamp collecting and bird watching.
Dislikes	Girls.
Character	Nerd. Always moaning about something.

ALIEN

Age	1,375 plobs (about 473 Earth years).
Likes	Conquering planets and sucking people's brains out.
Dislikes	All other forms of intelligent life and Nerds.
Character	Slimiest Alien in the Galaxy.

SQUIRT

Glue

Scene One

The kitchen in Melvyn's house.

MELVYN: Here we are, three lovely cups of warm cocoa.

FERGUS: Lovely.

MELVYN: I'll put them down here.

RODNEY: Hey, watch out! You'll spill that cocoa on my stamp album.

MELVYN: Oops.

(He spills cocoa on Rodney's stamp album.)

RODNEY: Told you.

FERGUS: Do you collect stamps?

RODNEY: Yes. Did you know that the Penny Pink is the most valuable stamp in the world?

FERGUS: I don't collect stamps.

MELVYN: You never know who's licked them.

FERGUS: You can get diseases.

MELVYN: It's too dangerous.

FERGUS: And too exciting. I collect milk bottle tops.

MELVYN: Ooh, let's see.

FERGUS: I've got them in this milk bottle top album.

MELVYN: Look, here's a silver one.

FERGUS: And here's another silver one.

RODNEY: Hey, guess what? A silver one!

FERGUS: What do you collect, Melvyn?

MELVYN: All sorts of stuff. Sticky backed plastic. Squeezy bottles. Ice-cream tubs. Egg cartons.

RODNEY: Egg cartons?

MELVYN: Yoghurt pots. Bits of old radio. Insides of old washing machines.

RODNEY: Don't be daft, you couldn't keep all that in an album.

MELVYN: I don't.

RODNEY: What have you done with it then?

MELVYN: I've made it into a spaceship.

FERGUS: A real spaceship?

MELVYN: Yeah.

RODNEY: One that really flies?

MELVYN: Yeah. They showed you how to do it on
           Blue Peter.

FERGUS: Where is it?

MELVYN: In the back garden. Do you want to see it?

RODNEY: Might as well.

FERGUS: But it's dark out there. There might be bats.

MELVYN: Come on.

Scene Two

On board Melvyn's spaceship.

FERGUS: Hey! This is so cool!

MELVYN: Yes, but it gets warmer when the rocket motor's on.

FERGUS: I meant ... never mind. How does it go?

MELVYN: Bottled gas. We use it for camping.

RODNEY: That's silly. You can't make a spaceship just out of ice-cream tubs and squeezy bottles and bits of junk.

MELVYN: Of course not.

RODNEY: Aha!

MELVYN: You need Sellotape and Blu-Tack as well!

FERGUS: I think it's a brilliant ship.

RODNEY: Has it got an on-board computer?

MELVYN: Yeah.

(He proudly produces a small computer game.)

RODNEY: That's just a game! It's not a real computer.

MELVYN: Oh dear! I suppose you'd like a Super PC
            with CD ROM and Internet access!

FERGUS: Don't argue, you two, it makes me go
            all wobbly. How does your spaceship
            work, Melvyn?

MELVYN: You see that big red lever over there?

FERGUS: You mean the one with a big notice over it
            that says "DANGER: DO NOT PULL
            THIS LEVER"?

MELVYN: That's the one. If you pull that lever, the ship will take off.

RODNEY: I bet somebody's going to pull that lever in a minute.

FERGUS: I want to look out of the window.

MELVYN: Look out, Fergus! You'll trip over that squeezy bottle.

(Fergus trips over the squeezy bottle. He staggers about waving his arms.)

FERGUS: Whoops!

MELVYN: Don't pull the lever, Fergus!

(Fergus pulls the lever. The ship takes off.)

RODNEY: Told you.

Scene Three

Inside the spaceship, an hour later. Melvyn is looking out of the window.

MELVYN: Space. The final frontier.

FERGUS: *(Pointing)* I thought this was the front, 'ere.

RODNEY: No, that's the back, there.

MELVYN: Our five year mission ...

FERGUS: I can't go on a five year mission! I told Mum I'd be back for tea!

MELVYN: ... is to boldly go where no man has boldly gone before.

RODNEY: You mean the ladies' toilets?

MELVYN: No! To the stars!

FERGUS: Ooer! I feel all light headed.

MELVYN: We must have gone into orbit.
We're weightless.

(Melvyn, Fergus and Rodney become weightless.)

FERGUS: I'm floating!

MELVYN: My mum said I should lose weight,
but this is ridiculous.

FERGUS: Where are we going, anyway?

MELVYN: I'm not exactly sure.

RODNEY: Well, why don't we look at the map?

MELVYN: Map?

RODNEY: Yes, map! You must have brought a map.
Only a nerd would go into space without
a map. Where is it?

MELVYN:	I didn't bring a map.
RODNEY AND	
FERGUS:	*(Together)* You nerd!
MELVYN:	Well, I didn't know we were going to take off, did I?
FERGUS:	How are we going to get back then?
MELVYN:	I don't know.
FERGUS:	What are we going to do?
MELVYN:	I don't know.
RODNEY:	I do. I know exactly what to do in this situation.
FERGUS AND	
MELVYN:	*(Together)* What?
RODNEY:	When in danger Or in doubt, Run in circles, Scream and shout!

(All three run around waving their arms about and shouting for help.)

13

MELVYN: This isn't getting us anywhere. Let's all calm down. Take deep breaths. In, two, three ... and out, two, three. In, two, three ... and out, two, three. In, two, three ... and out, two, three. In, two, three ...

RODNEY: Melvyn, why are we doing this?

MELVYN: It helps you to relax.

(As they talk, Fergus is still trying to hold his breath. He starts to turn red in the face.)

RODNEY: Does it?

MELVYN: Oh, yes.

RODNEY: Well, I don't feel very relaxed.

MELVYN: You have to keep doing it.

RODNEY: How long for?

MELVYN: Until you feel relaxed.

RODNEY: But how will I know when I feel relaxed?

MELVYN: You'll feel very calm. And sleepy.

RODNEY: (Yawning) Will I?

MELVYN: Yes, very sleepy. (Yawns.)

RODNEY: I think I'm starting to feel relaxed now ...

(Melvyn and Rodney keep yawning and nearly falling asleep, until they realize that Fergus is going purple, trying not to breathe.)

MELVYN: FERGUS, YOU CAN BREATHE NOW!

(Fergus lets out his breath in a great whoosh and pants.)

FERGUS: I don't want to relax any more, it's too dangerous.

MELVYN: All right, let's play "I Spy".

FERGUS: Oh, goodie.

MELVYN: Right. I spy with my little eye, something beginning with 'S'.

RODNEY: *(Bored)* Space.

FERGUS: Oh, well done, Rodney! Your go.

RODNEY: I spy with my little eye, something else beginning with 'S'.

MELVYN: Stars. My go. I spy with my little eye, yet another thing beginning with 'S'.

RODNEY: Sun.

FERGUS:	I want a go! I want a go!
MELVYN:	It's not your turn, you didn't get the answer.
FERGUS:	I want a go!
RODNEY:	Oh, all right.
FERGUS:	I spy with my little eye, something beginning with 'G A B'.
MELVYN:	'G A B'? What sort of a clue is that?
RODNEY:	Great Aunt Betty?
FERGUS:	No.
RODNEY:	Er ... Grubby Ant's Bottom.
FERGUS:	Close. But no.
MELVYN:	What is it then?
FERGUS:	Giant Alien Battleship.
RODNEY:	Giant Alien Battleship? Where?

(Fergus points out of the window.)

FERGUS: There!

MELVYN: Ooer. Rodney, he's right, there *is* a Giant Alien Battleship!

RODNEY: I bet it's going to open fire on us.

(The spaceship is hit. Melvyn, Fergus and Rodney are thrown about.)

RODNEY: Told you.

FERGUS: Full power to the ray guns!

MELVYN: We haven't got any ray guns. Sorry.

RODNEY: Missiles?

MELVYN: Nope. I've got this, though.

(He produces a packet of chalk.)

FERGUS: That's chalk! You can't hurt them with that!

MELVYN: Our teacher can. He can hit people on the ear, from the other side of the classroom.

RODNEY: Your teacher's not here, is he? Look out, they're firing again!

(The ship is hit again.)

MELVYN: We're out of control!

RODNEY: Do something!

FERGUS: I spy with my little eye, something beginning with 'D B P'.

RODNEY: You've had your go! What is it?

FERGUS: Dirty Big Planet.

MELVYN: What? Where?

(Fergus points out of the window.)

FERGUS: Out there.

RODNEY: I bet we crash into it.

(They crash into the planet.)

18

Scene Four

On the planet.

RODNEY: Told you.

FERGUS: We could be stuck here ... forever.

MELVYN: Just think! We're the first human beings to
           walk on the surface of another planet!

FERGUS: Spoooooky!

➔ *(Enter the Alien. It creeps about so that Melvyn, Fergus
and Rodney can't see it.)*

MELVYN: Well, I suppose we should just wait here to
          be rescued.

RODNEY: Who's going to rescue us? Nobody even
          knows we're here.

MELVYN: Ooer. I hadn't thought of that.

RODNEY: You know what they say, don't you?

MELVYN: What?

RODNEY: "In space, no one can hear you scream."

(Fergus sees the Alien and screams.)

MELVYN: I heard that.

RODNEY: Yeah. It must be wrong then.

FERGUS: I spy with my little eye, something
            beginning with 'S G A'.

MELVYN: That's easy. Slimy Green Alien.

FERGUS: Yes!

(They all turn round, see the alien, and scream.)

ALIEN: Doo wah diddy diddy dum diddy do!

FERGUS: What did he say?

MELVYN: He must be speaking Alien. I'll use
            my translator.

(He takes an electronic translator out of his pocket and keys in the Alien words.)

FERGUS: That's a calculator!

MELVYN: No, it's a translator.

FERGUS: Hey! That's cool.

MELVYN: Yes, I got it out of a catalogue. It does French, German and Alien. It gives you crossword clues as well. *(He reads the translation.)* Oh dear.

RODNEY: I bet it says it wants to take over our world.

MELVYN: *(Reading from the translator)* "I want to take over your world".

RODNEY: Told you.

ALIEN: Ooh bla di ooh bla da!

(Melvyn keys this in while Rodney speaks.)

RODNEY: I suppose it wants to suck our brains out first.

MELVYN: *(Reading from the translator)* "But I'm going to suck your brains out first."

RODNEY: Told you.

(The Alien prepares its dreadful mind-sucking device.)

FERGUS: Help!

RODNEY: I wish you hadn't bothered with that
             translator.

MELVYN: Run!

(They start to run, but the Alien zaps them with its freeze-gun.)

FERGUS: It's shot us with a freeze-gun!

MELVYN: I can't move.

RODNEY: Neither can I.

MELVYN: Oh, no, here it comes!

(The Alien grabs Melvyn and puts the brainsucking device on his head. Melvyn goes cross-eyed as his brain is sucked out.)

ALIEN: Oooooeeeeeeiiiiiii ... I hate football, oooee, trainspotting is brill ... a model engine ran for over 1200 hours and pulled six coaches over 1400 kilometres or 900 miles ... pink anoraks ... Mickey Mouse alarm clocks ... ooooo!!!

(The Alien moves on to suck Fergus's brain.)

ALIEN: Aaaaaaaiiiiiiiieeeeee ... the biggest sand castle ever built was over six metres high ... wellie boots ... fluffy dice ... woolly bobble hats!!!

24

(The Alien moves on to Rodney's brain.)

ALIEN: Oooooeeerrrrr ... what football team do
             starlings support? Starling Albion ... oooo
             ... Here's another interesting fact, did you
             know that the longest ever flight by a paper
             aeroplane was 17.2 seconds ...
             AAAAAARRRRRRRRRRRRGGGGGGGG
             HHHHHHHH!

(The Alien staggers away. Melvyn, Fergus and Rodney find they can move.)

FERGUS: Oooh, that was CREEPY!

MELVYN: Funny – we've all had our brains sucked out, but I don't feel any different.

RODNEY: Neither do I.

FERGUS: Nor me.

ALIEN: Excuse me ...

MELVYN: You can speak English now!

ALIEN: Yes, I learned it while sucking your brains out. Sorry about that by the way. It wasn't a very nice thing to do.

FERGUS: Oh, never mind.

ALIEN: I must say, your brains were full of the most interesting facts. I never realized how exciting milk-bottle top collecting could be, and now I know all about the mating habits of the common frog and how electric trains work and EVERYTHING!

MELVYN: Do you see what's happened? Sucking our brains out has turned him into one of us!

RODNEY: But I thought you were going to conquer the Earth.

ALIEN: Oh no, I don't like the sound of that at all, much too dangerous.

MELVYN: It looks as if we've saved the world.

FERGUS: Hurrah!

MELVYN: They'll probably give us all medals.

RODNEY: If we ever get back.

ALIEN: I must start a slime collecting club, and go
            spaceship-spotting ...

MELVYN: Excuse me, Mr Alien.

ALIEN: Please, call me Slimy.

MELVYN: Could you give us a lift home, please?

ALIEN: Well, I don't know, it's a long way and I've
            only just polished my flying-saucer ...

MELVYN: Please?

ALIEN: Oh, all right.

(Melvyn, Fergus and Rodney cheer.)

ALIEN: But first I've got to nip over to the Milky
            Way to see Mummy, then I've got a parcel
            to drop off at the next galaxy.

RODNEY: How long will that take?

ALIEN: About seventy of your Earth years.

MELVYN, RODNEY

AND FERGUS: *(Together)* What?

ALIEN: But don't worry. Think of all the interesting conversations we can have. Come on, let's have a singsong.

One man went to fly,

Went to fly a saucer ...

(Melvyn, Rodney and Fergus join in.)

ALL: One man and his droid,

Went to fly a saucer.

Scene Five

Melvyn's garden. Melvyn, Rodney, Fergus and the Alien come on singing.

ALL: Eight hundred and thirty three billion,
six hundred and seventy four million,
two hundred and forty eight thousand,
seven hundred and sixty three men went
to fly,
Went to fly a saucer ...

ALIEN: Here we are!

RODNEY: At last!

ALIEN: Well, must fly. Don't be strangers, now. Ta-ta!

(The Alien goes.)

RODNEY: We've been away for seventy years. Everybody we knew will be dead.

MELVYN: Not exactly. You see, as you get close to the speed of light, time gets slower.

FERGUS: So although we've saved the world and been halfway round the universe ...

MELVYN: On Earth, only a few hours have passed. Exactly.

RODNEY: But then, nobody will believe us.

FERGUS: I don't really believe it myself.

RODNEY: What if the whole thing was only a dream?

MELVYN: Aha! But I picked up part of our crashed
           spaceship. If it was only a dream, how do
           you explain this?

*(Melvyn whips his hand from behind his back. He holds
out a plastic squeezy bottle. Fergus and Rodney turn to
the audience.)*

FERGUS AND

RODNEY: *(Together)* Wow!